ASL Concepts Presents

American Sign Language
ABC WRITING
Workbook

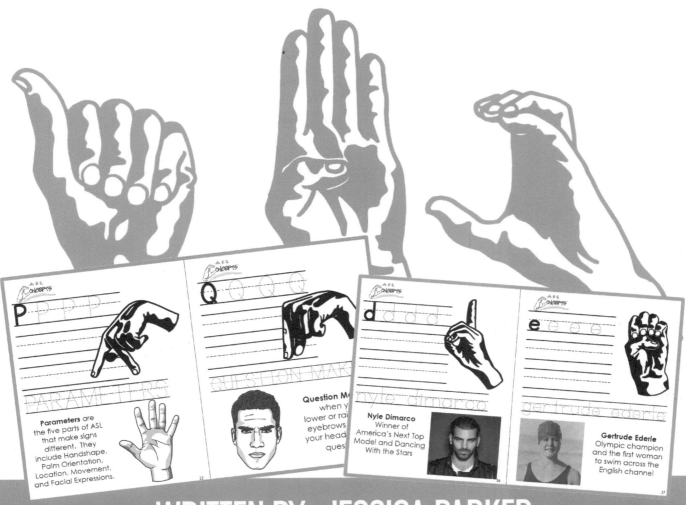

Parameters are the five parts of ASL that make signs different. They include Handshape, Palm Orientation, Location, Movement, and Facial Expressions.

Question M... when y... lower or rai... eyebrows... your head... ques...

Nyle Dimarco Winner of America's Next Top Model and Dancing With the Stars

Gertrude Ederle Olympic champion and the first woman to swim across the English channel!

WRITTEN BY: JESSICA PARKER

ASL Concepts Presents...
American Sign Language
ABC Writing Workbook

By
Jessica L. Parker

Illustrations by:
Joshua S. Patton

ASL Concepts
12134 Woodchase Circle
Anchorage, AK 99516
www.aslconcepts.com
aslconceptsak@gmail.com

Copies may be purchased from
ASL Concepts
12134 Woodchase Circle
Anchorage, Alaska 99516
www.aslconcepts.com
aslconceptsak@gmail.com
1-844-667-3524

First printing 2016
Second printing 2017

Acknowledgements

There are a number of loyal people involved in creating this workbook. Thank you to Josh Patton for your continued brilliance in creating original artwork for ASL Concepts curriculum. Thank you to my husband, Jeremy, for his efforts in supporting my work and editing my manuscripts. Thank you to Freepik for your certificate template. Thank you to my ASL Concepts Facebook Page supporters for your many words of encouragement and feedback. And thanks to the many educators who dedicate themselves to teaching American Sign Language to Deaf and hearing students.

"It is my hope that we will all love and guard our beautiful sign language as the noblest gift God has given to deaf people." - Geroge Veditz (1913)

Table of Contents

Acknowldegements-------------------4
Introduction-------------------------5
ASL Alphabet------------------------6
English Alphabet---------------------7
Capital Letters--------------------8-33
Lowercase Letters--------------34-59
Featured Deaf Terms----------------60
Featured Famous Deaf People-----61
Famous Deaf People Matching-----62
Deaf Culture Matching-------------63
Certificate-------------------------64
All About the Author/Illustrator----65

Introduction

This American Sign Language ABC Writing Workbook is designed to be used with ASL Concepts curriculum, specifically complementing *Chicka Chicka Boom Boom ASL Curriculum* perfectly. But it can also be used as a supplement to any Kindergarten through 2nd grade curriculum. It introduces the American Sign Language fingerspelled alphabet, while also teaching ASL grammar, Deaf history, and Deaf culture. Students will enjoy practicing essential skills such as recognizing letters, tracing and writing letters, learning to associate written letters with the signed alphabet, and improving fine motor skills. All of the activities are aligned with National ACTFL (American Council on the Teaching of Foreign Languages) and Common Core standards.

The workbook features capital letters along with a description of an ASL concept and an illustration. The lowercase letters feature a famous Deaf person along with a description and a picture. The final pages offer some additional activity and assessment materials, along with a Certificate of Achievement for completion.

How to Guide Young Minds
- Decide how many pages students will work on each day.
- Sign the ASL letters together.
- Go over the information on the pages and discuss together.
- Remind students how to hold a pencil and form the letters.
- Have students trace letters first before working independently.
- Give students praise and encouragement, circling their best letters.
- Use the matching activities as an assessment to chart their progress.
- Once students have completed all the pages, present them with the Certificate of Achievement.

ACTFL and Common Core Standards
- Interpersonal-Students can sign the ASL alphabet.
- Interpretive-Students can recognize the ASL alphabet when signed to them.
- Presentational-Students can write their capital and lowercase letters in English and present the matching letter in ASL.
- Cultures-Students can match Deaf culture terms and famous Deaf people correctly.
- CCSS.ELA-LITERACY.RF.1-demonstrate understanding of the organization and basic...
- CCSS.ELA-LITERACY.R1.4-ask and answer questions about unknown words in a text.
- CCSS.ELA-LITERACY.R1.7-describe the relationship between illustrations and the text ...
- CCSS.ELA-LITERACY.L.1-demonstrate command of the conventions of standard English...
- CCSS.ELA-LITERACY.L.5-explore word relationships and nuances in word meanings.
- CCSS.ELA-LITERACY.SL.4-describe familiar people, places, things, and events and, with...

American Sign Language Alphabet

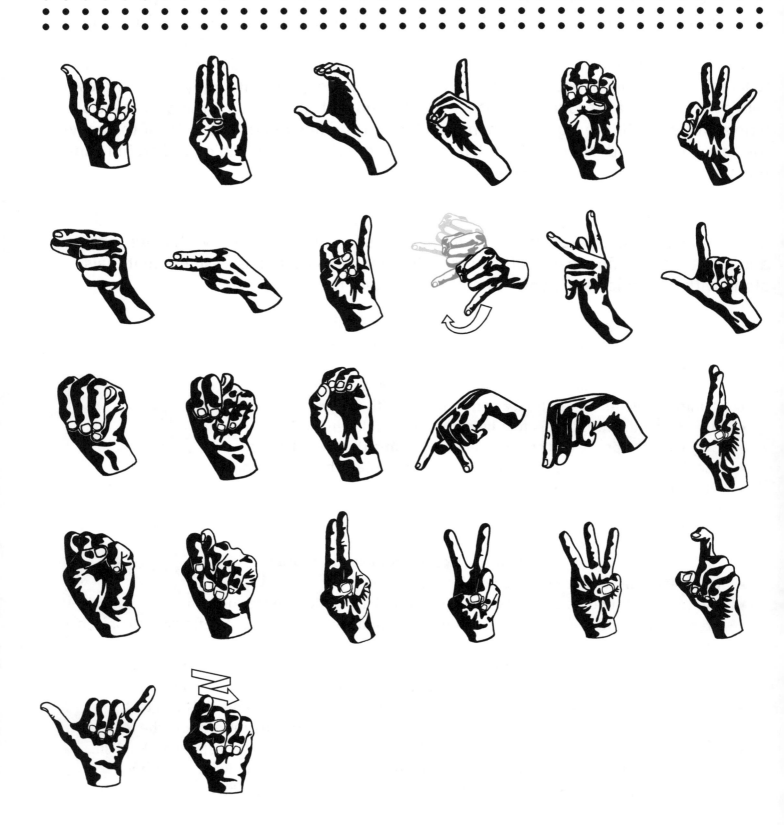

The English Alphabet

A B C D E F
G H I J K L
M N O P Q R
S T U V W X
Y Z

a b c d e f g
h i j k l m n o
p q r s t u v
w x y z

A A A A A

ASL

American Sign Language is a visual language made with your hands used by the Deaf to communicate.

B B B B

BOOK

There are many great **books** you can read to learn about ASL and Deaf culture.

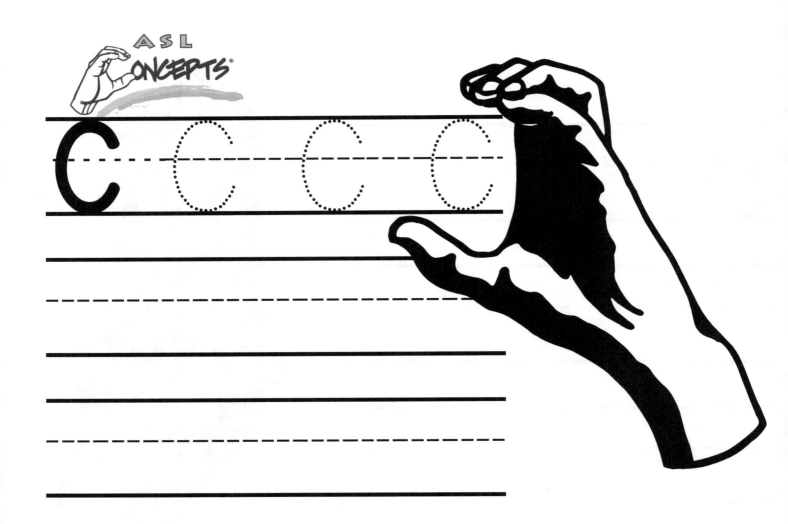

C C C C

CLOSED CAPTIONS

Closed Captions are words that appear on television or movie screens so the Deaf can understand what is being said.

D D D D D

DEAF

Deaf with a capital D is a cultural group of deaf people who use American Sign Language to communicate.

E E E E E

EYEBROWS

Eyebrows are an important part of American Sign Language grammar. They show that you are asking a question.

F

FINGERSPELLING

Fingerspelling is when you spell out words using the ASL alphabet.

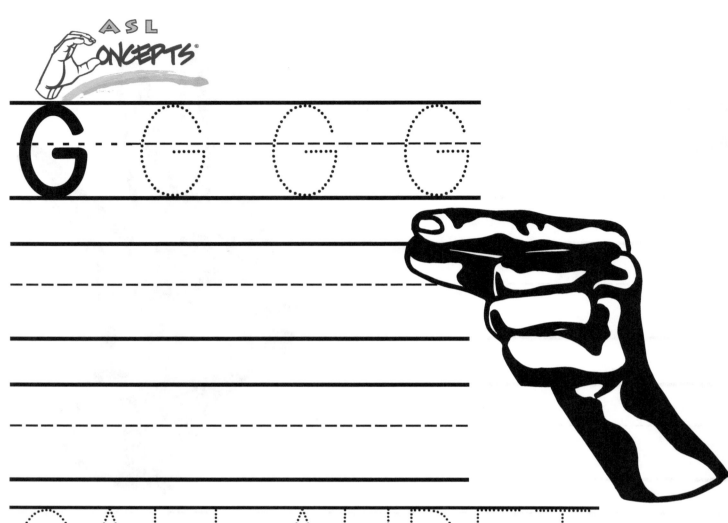

G   G   G   G

GALLAUDET

Gallaudet was the first school for the Deaf. It is now a University named after a man who helped create ASL.

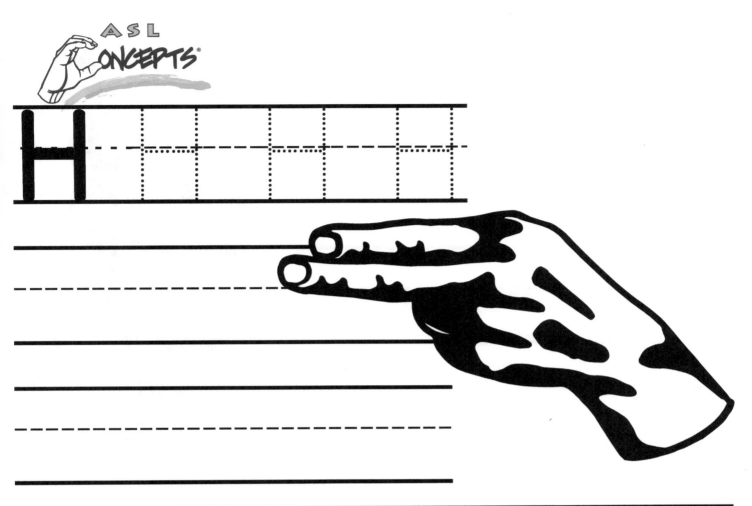

H

H E A R I N G   A I D E

A **hearing aide** is a device worn in the ear to make sounds louder.

I

INTERPRETER

An **interpreter** is a person who explains to a Deaf person what is said in ASL.

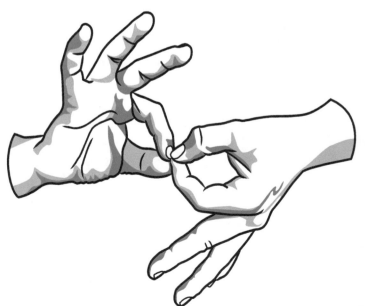

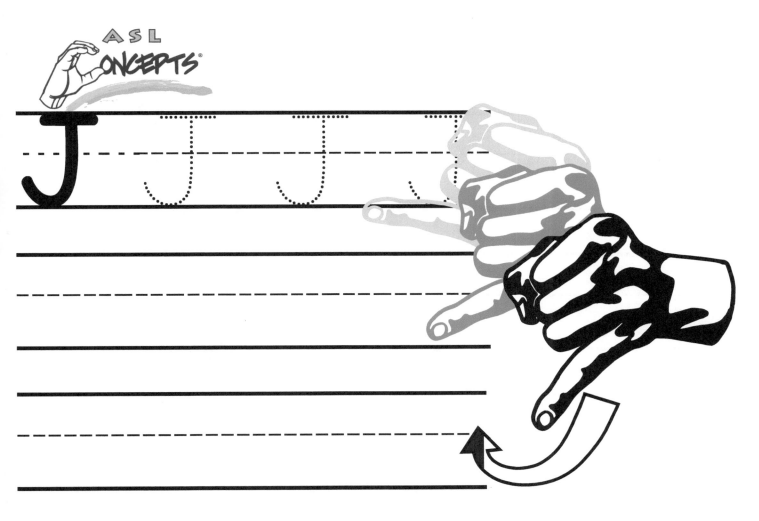

J J J J J

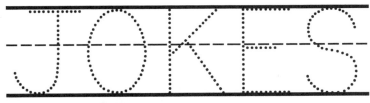

JOKES

That Deaf Guy
By Matt and Kay Daigle

A **Deaf joke** is a type of ASL literature based on Deaf experiences and the use of ASL.

K K K K K

KOKO

Koko the gorilla
can communicate
in ASL, and knows
over 1,000 signs.

L

LISTING TECHNIQUE

The **listing technique** is a visual list on your hand. You point to your list, then sign the information. It is a way to separate information.

M M M M M M M

MUSIC

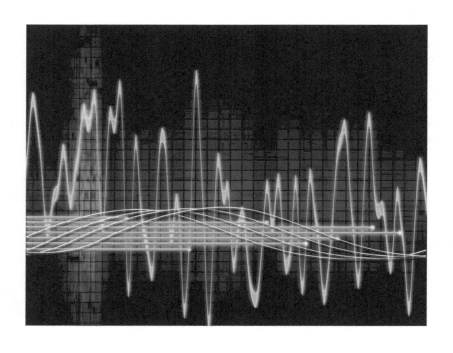

The Deaf can enjoy **music** by feeling the vibrations.

N N N N N

N A M E S I G N S

Name Signs are given by a Deaf person. It is considered an honor to receive a name sign in Deaf culture.

ORALISM

Oralism is teaching deaf people to communicate using lipreading and speaking, not signing.

P P P P

PARAMETERS

Parameters are the five parts of ASL that make signs different. They include Handshape, Palm Orientation, Location, Movement, and Facial Expressions.

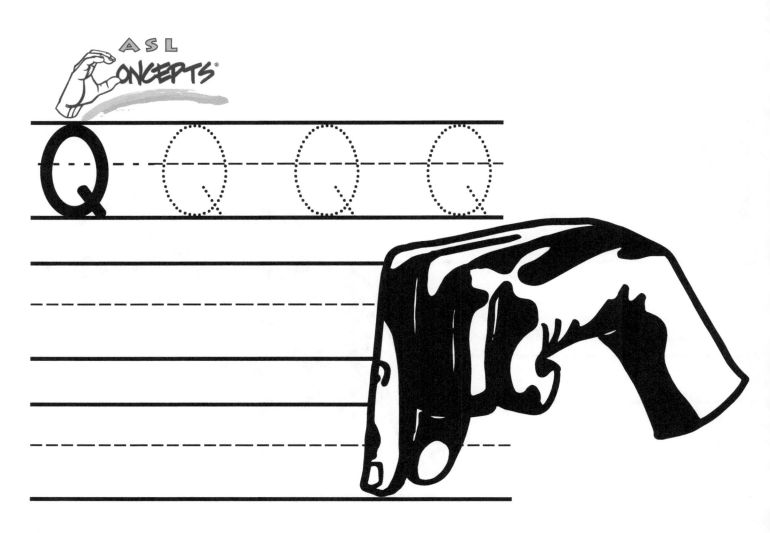

Q   Q   Q   Q

QUESTION MAKER

Question Maker is when you lower or raise your eyebrows and tilt your head to ask a question.

R R R R R

ROLE SHIFTING

Role Shifting is used when you sign a story. By shifting your body to one side, you become that character and the audience knows who is doing the action or talking. Shift your body to the other side to become a different character.

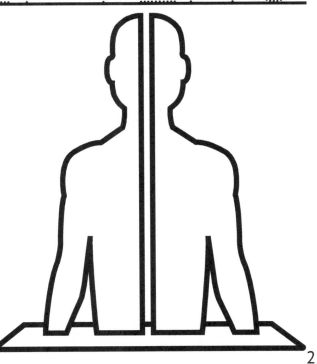

S   S   S   S

SIGNING SPACE

Signing Space is the signer's head, chest, and 12 inches to the left and right of the body.

26

Technology such as texting, captioning, and video phones can help the Deaf communicate with the hearing and provide them with access to information.

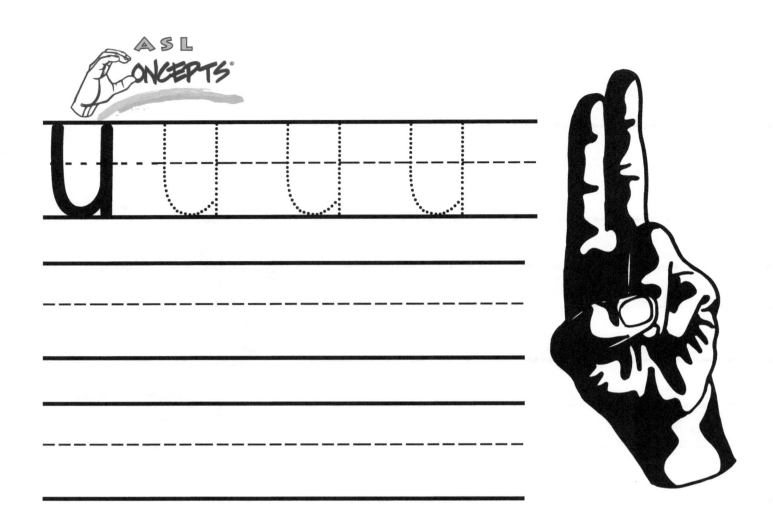

U U U U U

UNIVERSAL SIGNS

There is no Universal sign language, but there are a few Universal accepted signs such as "I Love You."

28

ASL CONCEPTS

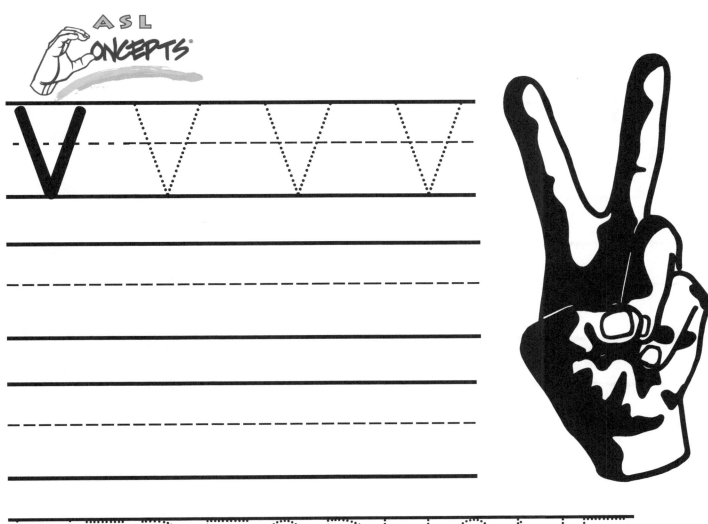

V V V V

VIDEOPHONE

Videophones allow the Deaf community to communicate with others in their natural language-ASL.

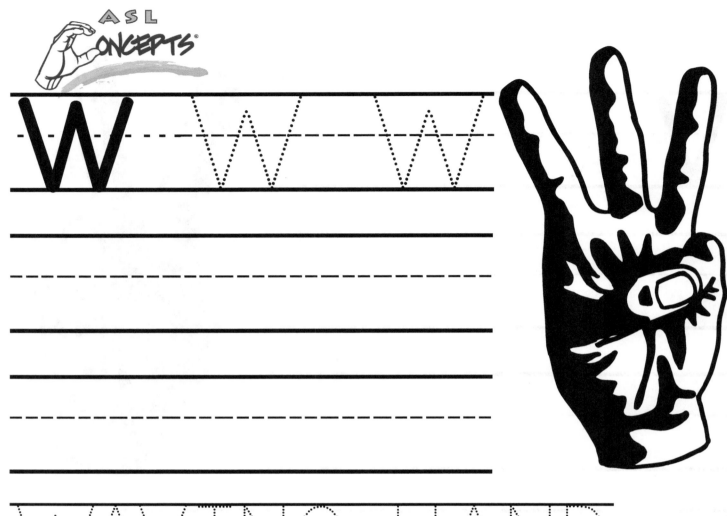

W W W

WAVING HAND

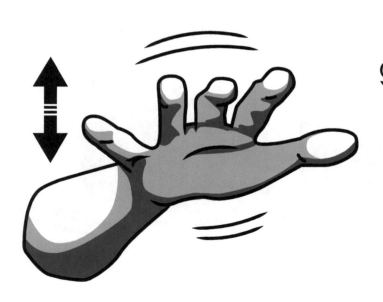

A common way to get a Deaf person's attention is to **wave your hand** at them. The movement will grab their attention.

X X X X X

EXPRESSION

Expression is an important part of ASL. It can change the meaning of a sign.

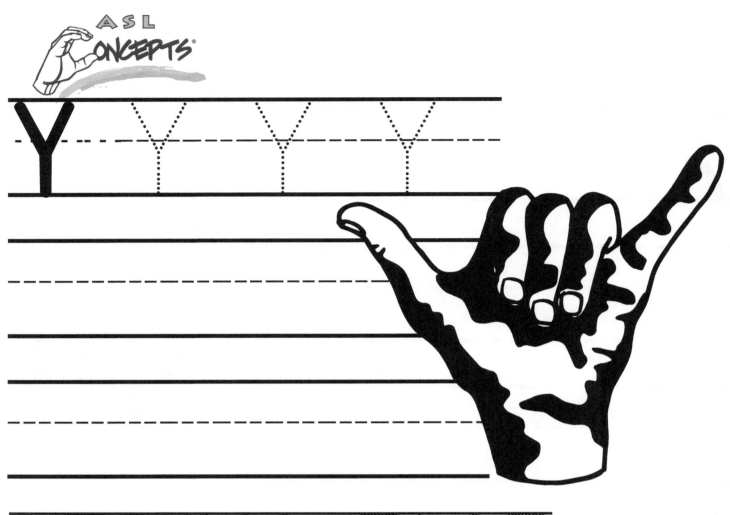

Y Y Y Y Y

YES NO FACE

The Yes/No Face is eyebrows up. This is used when asking a Yes/No question.

ZVRS

ZVRS was the first company in the United States to provide videophones. They also have interpreters and other services for the Deaf.

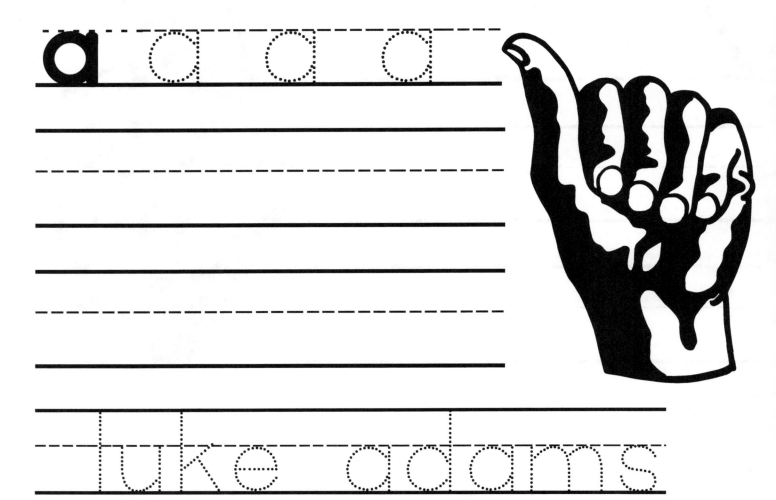

a a a a

luke adams

Luke Adams
Finalist on the
reality TV show
The Amazing
Race

34

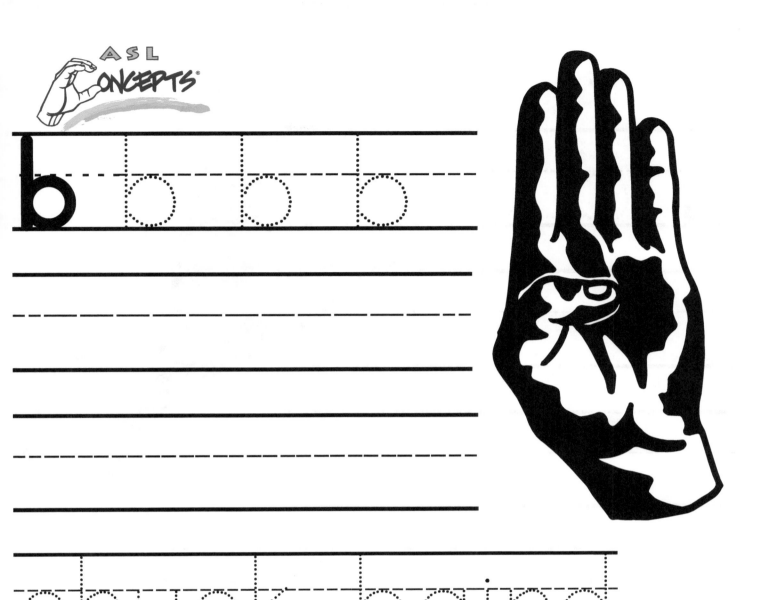

b b b b

chuck baird

Chuck Baird
Notable artist and
founder of the
DeVia art
movement

C c c c

laurent clerc

Laurent Clerc
Teacher who moved from France to America to establish the first school for the Deaf

d d d d

n y l e   d i m a r c o

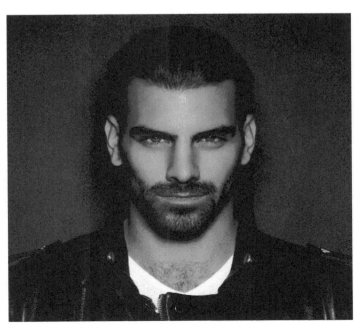

Nyle Dimarco
Winner of
America's Next Top
Model and Dancing
With the Stars

e   e   e   e

gertrude ederle

Gertrude Ederle
Olympic champion
and the first woman
to swim across the
English channel

f f f f f

ashley fiolek

Ashley Fiolek
Four-time
motorcross
racing
champion

g g g g

evelyn glennie

Evelyn Glennie
First solo
percussionist, plays
barefoot to feel
the vibrations

h

h h h h

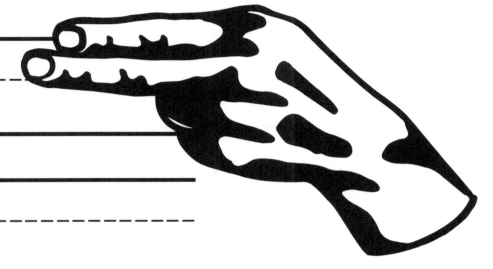

russell harvard

Russell Harvard
Actor, dancer,
and member of
the Bison Song
Team

41

i · · · · · · · · · · · · · · · · · · ·

izrael deutsch

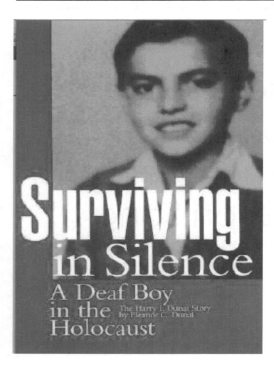

Surviving in Silence
A Deaf Boy in the Holocaust
The Harry I. Dunai Story
by Eleanor C. Dunai

Izrael Zachariah
Deutsch
Jewish Holocaust
survivor and
author

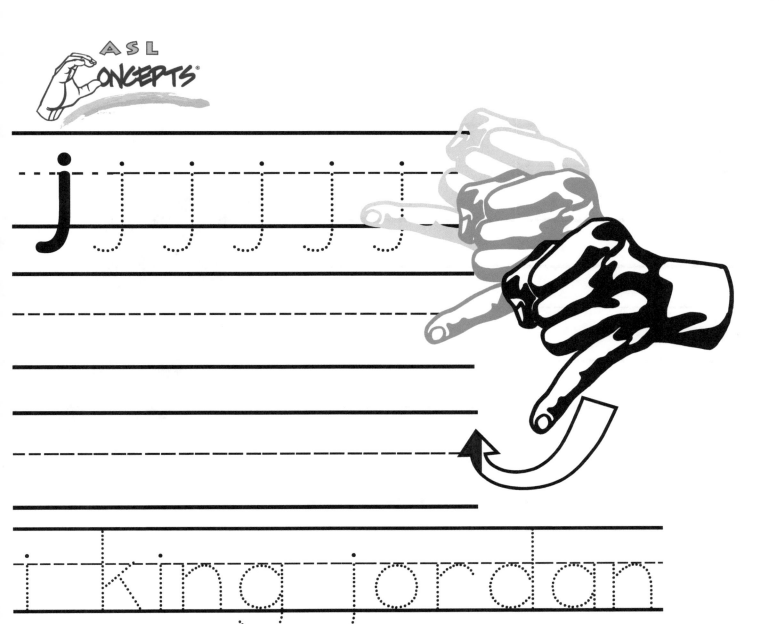

j j j j j j

i king jordan

Dr. Irving King Jordan
First Deaf president of Gallaudet University

k k k k k

helen keller

Helen Keller
Deaf and blind
author and
inspirational leader

juliette gordon low

Juliette Gordon Low
Youth leader and
founder of the Girl
Scouts

m m m m m

marlee matlin

Marlee Matlin
Author and
Academy award
winning actress

n n n n n n

malcolm norwood

Malcolm Norwood
Called the Father of Closed Captioning because of his work making captioning available on TV and film

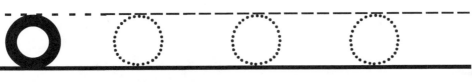

kitty o'neil

Kitty O'Neil
Racer and
stuntwoman who
starred in several
movies

p p p p

marie jean phillips

Marie Jean Phillips
A leader in Deaf Education and ASL teacher

q q q q

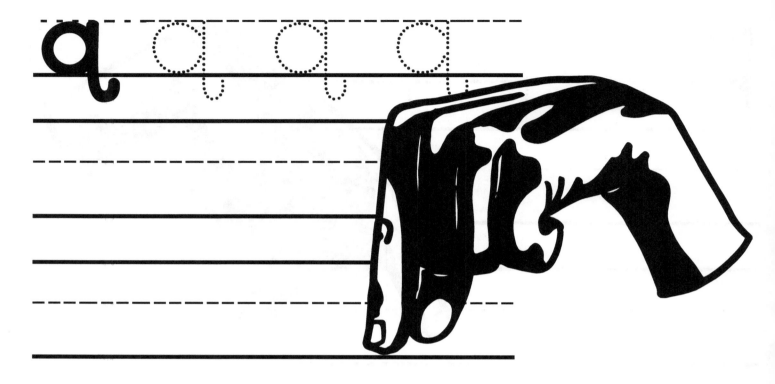

will quinlan

Will Quinlan
Artist whose work is featured in galleries and museums nation-wide

r r r r r r

cal rodgers

Cal Rodgers
First Deaf pilot and
first person to fly an
airplane across a
continent

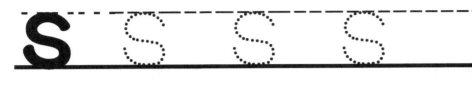

S S S S

ann silver

Ann Silver
Artist and
founder of the
Deaf Art
Movement

sue thomas

Sue Thomas
Worked as an undercover lipreading specialist for the F.B.I., a TV show called F. B. Eye was created based on her life

u u u u

ildiko ujlaky-rejto

**Ildiko Ujlaky-Rejto
Seven-time
Olympic fencing
champion**

V v v v v v

george veditz

George Veditz
Helped to preserve ASL with film and served as President of the National Association for the Deaf

W w w

heather whitestone

Heather Whitestone
Miss America
in 1995

X X X X X

trix bruce

Trix Bruce
Storyteller, poet,
actress, and ASL
instructor

y   y   y   y

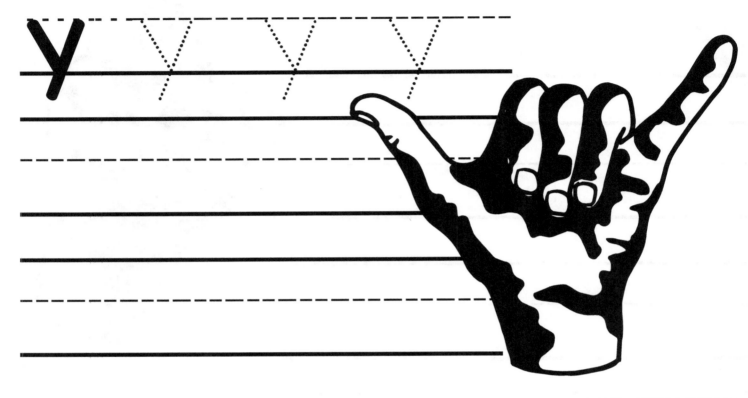

william "dummy" hoy

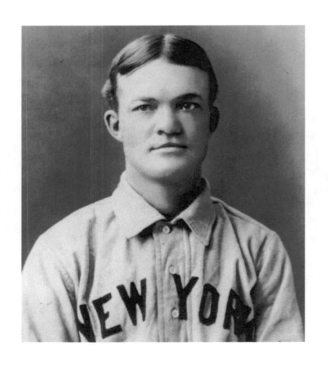

William "Dummy" Hoy
First Deaf professional baseball player and inventor of baseball hand signals

z Z Z Z Z Z Z

mike zupan

Mike Zupan
First Deaf professional
basketball player in
Europe

Featured Deaf Culture Terms

- ASL (American Sign Language)
- Book
- Closed Captions
- Deaf
- Eyebrows
- Fingerspelling
- Gallaudet
- Hearing Aide
- Interpreter
- Jokes
- Koko
- Listing Technique
- Music
- Name Signs
- Oralism
- Parameters
- Question Maker
- Role-Shifting
- Signing Space
- Technology
- Universal Signs
- Videophone
- Waving Hand
- eXpression
- Yes/No Face
- ZVRS

Featured Famous Deaf People

Famous Deaf People Matching

1. First professional Deaf baseball player and inventor of hand signals

2. Founder of the Girl Scouts

3. First Deaf pilot and first person to fly an airplane across a continent

4. Racer and stuntwoman who starred in several movies.

5. Finalist on the TV show "Amazing Race"

6. Notable artist and founder of the DeVia art movement

7. Storyteller, poet, actress, and ASL storyteller

8. Winner of *America's Next Top Model* and *Dancing with the Stars*.

9. Author and Academy award winning actress

10. Four-time motorcross champion

A) Juliette Gordon Low

B) Chuck Baird

C) Nyle Dimarco

D) Kitty O'Neil

E) Trix Bruce

F) Ashley Fiolek

G) Cal Rodgers

H) Marlee Matlin

I) Luke Adams

J) William "Dummy" Hoy

Deaf Culture Terms Matching

1. A common way to get a Deaf person's attention

2. The five parts that make up ASL

3. A group of deaf people who use ASL to communicate

4. A visual language made on the hands used by the Deaf to communicate

5. Eyebrows up, used to ask a specific type of question

6. A type of ASL literature based on Deaf experience and ASL

7. A gorilla that can communicate in ASL

8. Words that appear on TV or movie screens so the Deaf can understand what is being said

9. The first school for the Deaf in America

10. Used to help the Deaf communciate with the hearing and provide access to information

A) Jokes

B) Koko

C) Parameters

D) Technology

E) Deaf

F) Gallaudet

G) Closed Captions

H) Waving Hand

I) Yes/No Question Face

J) American Sign Language

CERTIFICATE

of

Achievement

Congratulations on finishing the American Sign Language ABC Writing Workbook!

ASL CONCEPTS

_____
Signature

_____
Date

Jessica Parker, Author

Founder of ASL Concepts, Jessica has over 20 years of ASL teaching experience. She holds a Bachelor's and Master's degree from Dallas Baptist University and is nearing completion of her Doctorate in Curriculum and Instruction. She teaches ASL in Anchorage, Alaska and has first-hand exposure within the Deaf community as a CODA (Child of a Deaf Adult). She also works as a curriculum consultant, helping other districts develop ASL programs and academic plans. With a passion for teaching and writing curriculum, Jessica aims to help develop successful ASL programs throughout the nation.

Josh Patton, Illustrator

Josh has a business degree from Wayland Baptist University. He has over 10 years of experience creating and sharing his artistic vision with others. Josh specializes in creating original artwork for businesses and individuals including: logos, t-shirt designs, posters, and video productions. For more information, or to get a quote, contact Josh at joshpatton@mail.com.

Together as a coda brother & sister team, Jessica and Josh are committed to creating relevant ASL curriculum and materials.

12134 Woodchase Circle
Anchorage, Alaska 99516
aslconceptsak@gmail.com
(844) 667-3524

ASL Concepts aims to provide excellent curriculum materials, instruction, and advocacy to the field of American Sign Language. Deaf culture is woven into every element of the curriculum. You can find more information about ASL Concepts curriculum at www.aslconcepts.com.

CHECK OUT ADDITIONAL ASL CONCEPTS MATERIALS AT WWW.ASLCONCEPTS.COM

- Based on Bill Martin Jr. and John Archambault's *Chicka Chicka Boom Boom*
- *Teaches the following ASL Concepts:*
  - *Fingerspelling Rules*
  - *Name Signs*
  - *Directionality*
  - *Classifiers 1 and 5*

- Based on P.D. Eastman's *Are You My Mother?*
- *Teaches the following ASL Concepts:*
  - *Pronouns*
  - *Yes/No Face*
  - *Head Nod/Head Shake*
  - *Listing Technique*
  - *Role-Shifting*

Made in United States
Troutdale, OR
07/23/2023